Puffin
Parable & Facts

written and illustrated by
mandy elizabeth rush

Puffin Parable and Facts

Puffin Species

There are believed to be only four different species of Puffin in the world. The Atlantic Puffin, Horned Puffin, Tufted Puffin and Rhinoceros Auklet.

However there are actually another two species of Puffin, which are very rare and only found in Scotland. These are the Bawheid and Dunderheid Puffin.

Bawheid and Dunderheid mean chubby faced and stupid person in Scots. Scottish folklore claims this is the real reason the Puffin got the nickname of 'clown of the sea'.

The Puffin's black and white plumage is said to be reminiscent of the robes of monks and because of this their scientific genus name is Fratercula meaning 'little brother' in Latin.

WANTED
DEAD or ALIVE
unfortunately

30cm — Perfectly Puffin

25cm — Pouting Puffin

20cm — Pious Puffin

15cm — Posing Puffin

10 cm — Pint Sized Puffin

5cm — Puffling

Perfectly Puffin

Our wee Atlantic Puffin is only 30 centimetres tall, about the same length as a ruler, with an average wingspan of 50 centimetres and weighing about the same as a can of Cola.

Despite their small size, Puffins are strong and powerful. They can dive as deep as 60 metres under water, remaining submerged for up to one minute; propelling themselves underwater with their strong sturdy wings and using their tails like rudders. Imagine Penguins who can fly.

In fact Happy Feet the Penguin movie was originally based on a screenplay about a colony of Puffins. Unfortunately the Puffin Trade Union, GULP (Global Union of Lovely Puffins), failed to reach an agreement with Hollywood about the Puffin's sand eel salary and the Penguins hooked the deal.

Groups of Puffins

Puffins are social birds especially around the mating season.

These large groups of Puffins have collected many names throughout the ages including Colony, Puffinry, Gathering, Circus and also an Improbability.

To put an end to this uncertainty about what to call a group of Puffins they organised a poll. The politic loving Puffins voted in their millions.

The referendum results were clear: Puffins live in a Gathering.

Puffin Fidelity

The monogamous Puffin mates for life when they become ready to make little Pufflings at the age of four or five.

The non-monogamous Puffin will also mate at the age of four or five but they are likely to cause a lot of trouble in the usually peaceful burrows of the Puffinry.

Beautiful Beak

Outwith the mating season, a Puffin's real beak is dull grey and quite bland. By April however their brightly coloured beaks have regrown and the mating rituals begin.

Intriguingly the masked vigilante Zorro is believed to be a Puffin in disguise. You may not have noticed that Zorro only reappears in September and disappears again in March each year; the months that correspond with a Puffin wearing his 'winter wardrobe'.

Courting Couples

After the winter months of fishing at sea, courting Puffins will pair up before they return to their nesting grounds.

Larger and larger rafts of Puffins gather off-shore waiting for the perfect conditions to begin the new season of egg laying.

The social little Puffins love this time of year, when they can catch up with family and friends. It's also the perfect time for the Puffin White Water Rafting and Free Style Diving Championships.

Gift Giving

Finally, all caught up and exhausted from the competitive sports, the Puffins decide to land on their chosen island. The courting pairs then begin beak rubbing or 'billing', preening and even a wee bit of head tossing.

Male Puffins sometimes make the ladies swoon with gifts of flowers, feathers or grass, which they tenderly present to their sweetheart in their brightly coloured bill.

Despite what you might think, just like snowflakes, no two Puffins are identical, especially to a Puffin.

The courtship rituals can often draw a large crowd of Puffins who watch and participate in the exciting display. The fun and games of Puffin pursuits often end in a ceilidh, where the Highland Gathering of Puffins dance the night away under the full moon.

The Perfect Home

Once happily paired and seduced by sensual billing, the Puffin pair begin to dig their burrow.

Puffins are, in fact, no clowns, they not only return to the same island and nesting site but also the same burrow they dug together the previous summer.

Typically these burrows are dug into soft soil and Puffins are quite happy to remodel vacated rabbit burrows. Sometimes they are even quite happy to evict the rabbits, the rabbits of course are decidedly not happy at this anti-social behaviour.

Where burrowing isn't possible, Puffins will nest under boulders or other holes in rocky shorelines.

Puffins are incredibly proud of their burrows. They dig curved passageways with their beaks and webbed feet and even have a separate chamber, at the first bend, which is used as a bathroom by the little chick.

The Bonniest Egg

Puffins lay just one lovely white egg which both parents incubate.

Sadly this low reproductive rate results in Puffins being very vulnerable to population decline.

The clever Puffins of the Shiant Isles (tiny Hebridean Islands) wrap their eggs up snuggly in warm Harris Tweed egg-cosies to keep their precious eggs extra warm.

Fluffy Puffling

Five to eight weeks later, the little fluffy Puffling pecks itself free of its shell.

Oh what a stramash you will then hear at the Gathering.

Puffins actually have a vocabulary of over a hundred calls, but to humans, two Puffins 'chatting' simply sound like two little mopeds revving their engines.

Feeding Baby

Both parents take turns catching many fish and sand eels to feed their little Puffling.

The amazingly beautiful beak of the Puffin can carry multiple fish crosswise. Therefore unlike most birds, the Puffin doesn't have to eat and regurgitate the food for their little Puffling. With special hinges and an upper and lower beak that meets at different angles, Puffins can keep stuffing fish into their mouth without them falling out.

Puffins have noticed how keen the Puffin Paparazzi (aka Tourists) are to catch a photo of them with their mouths full, therefore, during the tourist season, Puffins work on a rota system to pose for tourist photographs.

Time to Tumble

Eventually, after weeks of feeding their hungry baby, Mummy and Daddy Puffin leave the Puffling home alone as they fly off to sea for the winter.

After seven or eight weeks in the burrow it's time for the little Puffling to leave their hideaway.

Our brave wee Puffling has been patiently waiting for the perfect conditions to leave their nest.

They can neither swim nor fly properly but they can float and paddle.

Like turtle hatchlings, Pufflings leave their nests on the same night under the protection of darkness. The date of departure is usually determined to coincide with the end of the Scottish School Summer Holidays. A time when the Puffins income from tourism significantly decreases.

They tumble towards the sea, guided by the reflections of the moon. When they reach the sea they start paddling to get as far from shore as possible before dawn.

Near Reykjavik, Iceland, the poor wee Pufflings get confused with the bright city lights and often miss the sea. Instead they end up on the icy city streets as they search for the wide ocean.

Ripe old Age

Puffins would like to live for at least 20 years, however threats to Puffins are many.

Originally their only natural predators were humans and gulls.
Now, due to the impact and actions of humans and introduced non-native fox, rat, mink and cat the Puffin population has been decimated.

Other significant factors killing our Puffins are pollution, overfishing and global warming.

Children today now believe Puffins got their name because of the high incidence of asthma now prevalent in all Huffing -Puffin populations. Before the spike in asthma suffering, Puffins were actually called Tammynories or Coulternebes in Scotland.

Asthma in Puffin populations is attributed to increased pesticide use and oil pollution. Just like humans the Puffins are prescribed red, yellow, blue and orange inhalers. Some Puffins actually pretend to have asthma as the chemicals in the colourful inhalers make their multi-coloured beaks extra vibrant and bright.

Puffin Pie

Puffins continue to be hunted for their meat in Iceland and the Faroe Isles where they have no legal protection.

Smoked Puffin is the Icelandic delicacy served in local restaurants and is normally served with bilberry or blueberry sauce.   Clever Puffins have now started an aerial campaign to poop on all bilberry and blueberry bushes in an act of resistance and terrorism.

At school, Puffins must watch the Alfred Hitchcock movie, The Birds, as part of their national curriculum, in the expectation that one-day they will rebel and fight against this Puffin genocide.   After all Puffins out number Icelanders 29:1.

Actually Puffins are highly allergic to Icelanders and they pray, that one day, Icelanders will become allergic to them!

Poor Wee Puffins

On the Icelandic Island of Heimaey all the road signs are shaped like Puffins. This is a cunning plan to confuse the poor Puffins who stop and ask these 'false' Puffins for directions as they try to escape 'sky fishing'.

Sky fishing is a form of Puffin hunting in Iceland where the defenceless wee Puffins are caught in large nets as they dive into the sea to catch their dinner.

Over fishing of sand eels and whitebait, typical Puffin food, is resulting in the starvation and death of our little clowns of the sea.

Climate change and sea temperature fluctuations negatively affect the Puffin's prey.

Nine out of ten of our Puffins have plastic inside their guts, which they gobble up as they fish. The poor birds think they are eating a proper meal, but they sadly have a tummy full of plastic.

From plastic bags, bottle caps, bits of balloons, cigarette lighters, toothbrushes, toys, all of these and more have been found in the birds' tummies.

Prevent Puffin Suffering
Pick up Three &
Save our Sea!

Further Puffin Facts or are they Fictions?

Puffins flap their wings 400 times a minute whilst flying. Not quite a Hummingbirds 80 times per second but an impressive blur nonetheless.

Aggravated Puffins 'puff up' and stamp their feet when they are grumpy with someone. Sometimes called a Fluffing Puffin.

All Scottish Puffins fail breathalyser tests due to having a naturally occurring small amount of whisky in their bloodstream, which stops them from freezing.

On the Isle of St. Kilda, Puffins were traditionally used to flavour porridge.

The Famous Grouse Whisky of Scotland was originally named the Famous Puffin Whisky but the poster boy Puffins loved the taste of the whisky too much and kept falling over at photo-shoots, therefore the Puffins were sent flapping.

Penguin Books, the famous publishing house, was founded by His Right Honourable Chesterfield Guffin McPuffin (A Tufted Puffin) in the 1940s. (He suffered from terrible flatulence).

To find out the answers go to:
www. mandyerush. me/puffin-facts-or-fictions

Glossary

Bawheid — (Scots) A person with a chubby face. A stupid person

Bonnie — (Scots) Beautiful, attractive

Ceilidh — (Scots) Social event with Scottish music, singing, traditional dancing, stories

Dunderheid — (Scots) Idiot, simpleton, eejit, numpty

Guff/ Guffing — (Scots) An unpleasant smell, smoke, farting

Hame — (Scots) Home

Highland Gathering — (Scots) Event with traditional Scottish dancing, music, and sports competitions

Parable — A simple story used to illustrate a moral or spiritual lesson

Stramash — (Scots) Commotion, uproar, a state of great excitement

Wee — (Scots) Small, tiny, little

Books by Mandy

Scottish Beastie Books:
Haggis History & Facts
Midge Myths & Facts
Puffin Parable & Facts

Gracie MacKay and her Toothfairie

Timmy Tails – a delightful collection of true stories
about Mandy's beloved 3 legged Ginger German Cat

The Dragon King of Yellowstone

Buy further books at:
Web: www. mandyerush. me
Email: mandyerush@me. com

Mandy Elizabeth Rush

Mandy lives in Melvaig, in 'The last house before the lighthouse', in the Highlands of Scotland.

She lives with her partner and their ginger chickens, The Weasleys, Araucana Amy and their five ducks, The Royal Duckesses called Argyll, Sutherland, Ross, Cromarty and Fife.

Mandy loves to write and illustrate books about the wonders of the Highlands where she is surrounded by Haggis friendly habitat. She protects several secret local Haggii holts.